This bite-sized bo
useful overview o
will help you to ac

- Raise awaren
  responses
- Understand stress and the effect it can have
- Commit to self-care and good habits
- Sustain a healthy and balanced lifestyle
- Replenish every day to maintain energy levels

The 21st century health epidemic

The World Health Organization has dubbed stress as the modern-day health epidemic. The fallout from workplace stress has a huge impact on global well-being as well as on our overall economy.

For a multitude of reasons the pace of modern life has accelerated. In a rapidly evolving world of too much choice and overwhelm it can be challenging to establish a healthy balance. Everyday pressures can build up and affect our stress levels without us even being aware that it is happening. The creep of burnout can be insidious.

Burnout is a state of emotional, physical and mental exhaustion caused by excessive and prolonged stress. It occurs when an individual feels overwhelmed, emotionally drained and unable to meet constant demands.

There is a greater recognition than ever before of the need to promote good mental health in the workplace and employers are being urged to treat mental and physical health with equal importance.

Whilst elevated stress isn't a mental health problem in itself, it can often lead to anxiety, depression, self-harm and suicide. It can also lead to physical health problems such as cardiovascular disease and joint and muscle problems.

This bite-sized book is designed to be a simple and practical guide to help you to manage stress and avoid burnout.

Stress Awareness

Everyday Energy

Stress Intelligence

Stress Knowledge

Lifestyle Management

Self-care

Stress intelligence - 5 stages

This model is about raising personal intelligence around stress and covers the following stages:

1. Stress awareness - raise awareness of your own relationship with stress by understanding your triggers and responses.

2. Stress knowledge - understand stress and the effect it can have on your mental and physical health.

3. Self care - commit to self-care and establish healthy boundaries and habits.

4. Lifestyle management - manage your well-being by maintaining a healthy and balanced lifestyle.

5. Everyday energy - create moments of sanctuary to replenish your everyday energy levels.

Stress Awareness

We are all unique and different types of pressure affect people in different ways. One size doesn't fit all when it comes to stress.

It is important to take time to analyse and understand your relationship with stress.

Ask yourself the following questions:

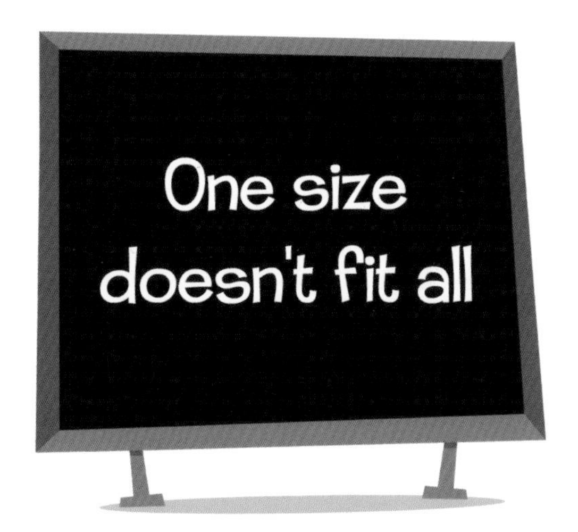

What are your stress triggers?

Stress management starts with identifying your sources of stress and developing strategies to manage them.

Lack of control, interruptions, frustration with technology, an overwhelming to-do list, changing priorities, information overload and other people's behaviour are all common triggers.

A constructive way to identify your triggers is to make a list of the situations, concerns or challenges that activate your stress response.

Take time to identify and write down some of the top issues you are experiencing in your life right now. You may notice that some of your stressors are events that are actually happening to you while others may even be your mind creating scenarios before they have actually happened.

What happens to you?

Too much stress in the body can trigger a range of physical and psychological responses. It is important to understand what happens to you so that you can identify the warning signs of burnout. You may be able to relate to some of the following:

- Increase in heart rate or palpitations
- Headaches and migraines
- Muscle tensions
- Fatigue and lack of energy
- Change in appetite
- Stomach upsets
- Sleep problems
- Anxiety, sadness or depression
- Lack of motivation or focus
- Irritability or anger
- Tearful and emotional outbursts

How do you manage your stress?

Everyone will have a different way of managing their stress levels. Some of the approaches you choose may not be helpful such as drinking alcohol, smoking, or reaching out for sugary or fatty foods.

Focusing on more healthy ways to manage your stress levels will be far more effective in the long-term.

Exercise, getting some fresh air, drinking water, spending time with friends, hobbies, having pets, mindfulness and music can all be effective and positive alternatives.

The first step to eliminating unhelpful coping mechanisms is to be aware of them and start to replace them with something more healthy. It is easy to make excuses and give in to reduced willpower, however this is the time you need to choose healthier coping mechanisms.

Stress
Knowledge

Understand stress

First of all, let's get one thing straight. Stress is not the enemy! More often than not, there seems to be such a negative connotation attached to stress, with some people even in pursuit of a stress-free life. This type of existence, however, is unrealistic because a certain level of stress is a prerequisite for actually staying alive.

Without any stress, our bodies and minds simply wouldn't be able to perform. Stress is a natural physiological and psychological reaction to a change to the body or the circumstances surrounding it. It is your body's way of responding to any kind of demand or unexpected pressure.

Learning to rein in and ride your stress will help you to feel much more in control.

Where does the term stress come from?

The term 'stress', as it is currently used, was coined in 1936 by a pioneering Hungarian endocrinologist called Hans Selye, who was known as the father of stress for his studies of the effects of stress on the human body. He defined stress as "the non-specific response of the body to any demand for change". He distinguished between two types of stress:

1. Eustress which when managed well is a positive stress that can lead to growth and enhanced competence. Sportspeople are a good example of where stress can be channelled in a constructive way.

2. Distress which is a negative stress that is uncontrollable, prolonged and overwhelming and can be destructive.

He also created the stress model General Adaptation Syndrome, which explains the stress response and how ageing and disease are caused by chronic exposure to stress. The General Adaptation Syndrome stress model has three stages.

General
Adaptation
Syndrome

1. Alarm stage

In this phase, the initial reaction of the body to stress is that it labels the stressor as a threat or danger to balance, which is why it immediately activates its fight or flight response system, and releases the "stress" hormones such as adrenaline, noradrenaline and cortisol.

These hormones enable you to perform activities that you don't usually do.

Stress experts around the world are now adding the word freeze in deference to the fact that instead of fighting or fleeing, sometimes you may freeze instead (like a deer in the headlights) in some traumatic situations.

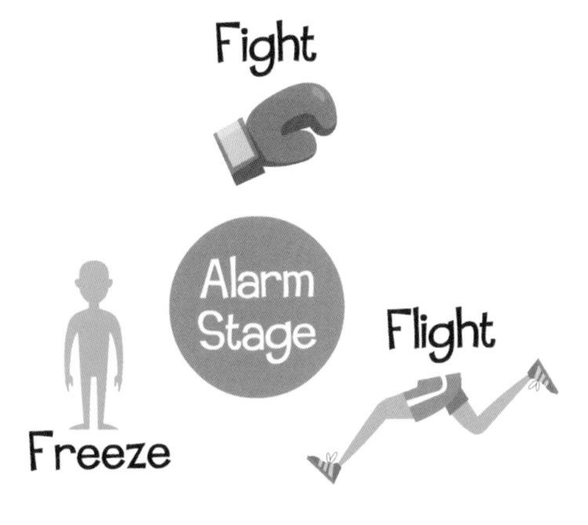

2. Resistance stage

After the body has responded to the stressor, it is most likely that the stress level has been eradicated, or simply reduced. What happens next to the stress response is that your body's defences become weaker because it needs to allocate energy to lower the production of the stress hormones.

3. Exhaustion stage

During this phase, the stress has been persistent for a longer period. The body starts to lose its ability to combat the stressor and reduce their harmful impact because the adaptive energy has been drained. The exhaustion stage can be refereed to as the gateway towards burnout and health problems if not resolved quickly.

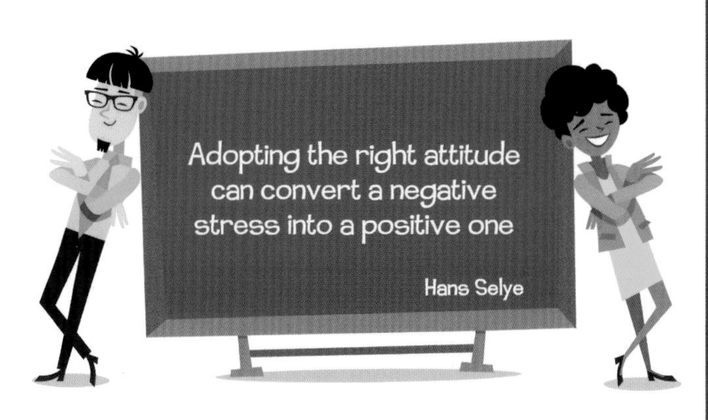
Adopting the right attitude
can convert a negative
stress into a positive one
Hans Selye

Self-care

Self-love, my liege,
is not so vile a sin,
as self-neglecting
William Shakespeare

When you put together your daily to do-list where do you feature on it? It is possible that you don't even get a look in! Factoring yourself in and making a commitment to create some "me time" by investing in self-care and establishing healthy boundaries and habits is essential in avoiding burnout.

Making your own personal well-being your biggest priority has nothing to do with being selfish. No one needs to feel guilty or ashamed about this. It is, in fact, the most responsible approach to life. If you spend your life running around after everyone else eventually you will burn yourself out and those people will then need to look after you!

What is the instruction on an aircraft when the flight attendants take you through the safety instructions?

Put the life mask on yourself before you help others!

Isn't that just a great analogy for life?

You may well have an inner superhero who likes to think they are super capable. It is really important when it comes to burnout to be realistic of your own capacity. You simply cannot be everything to everybody.

People-pleasing is something that happens when you want people to like you or approve of what you do. It can be hard to say no and then you end up taking on far too much.

There may well be occasions where you have to be assertive and protect your depleted energy levels by saying, "Whilst I would love to help you, at the moment I simply don't have the capacity to do this."

On some occasions it may not necessarily be a case of saying no you may well say yes, however, on your terms!

Remember, ultimately the most important person you need to seek approval from is yourself.

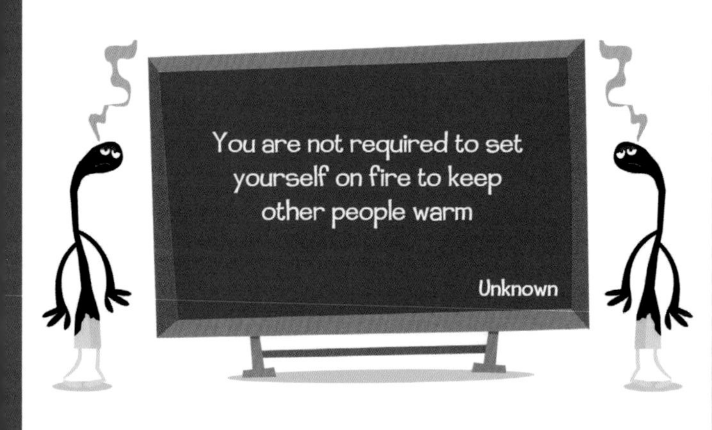
You are not required to set yourself on fire to keep other people warm
Unknown

Personal boundaries are essential to healthy relationships and managing unnecessary stress. Having healthy boundaries is about knowing and understanding what your limits are.

To set healthy boundaries you need to know where you stand by identifying your physical, emotional, mental and spiritual limits. You need to consider what you can tolerate and accept and what makes you feel uncomfortable or stressed.

Boundaries are a sign of a healthy relationship and they are also a sign of self-respect.

Putting yourself first also gives you the energy, peace of mind and positive outlook to be more present with others and be there for them.

It is essential to give yourself the permission to set boundaries and work to preserve them.

When it comes to self-care it is so important to take personal responsibility for your well-being. It is also about making a conscious decision and commitment to look after yourself.

Next time you hear yourself saying "I have to do this or I need to do this," replace those words with "I choose to do this!"

Remember, the pressure we put ourselves under very often is much more than anyone else would.

We can at times, if we are not careful, be our own worst taskmaster!

It is really important to nourish yourself and set realistic and achievable expectations.

Sometimes, just getting things done is better than the gruelling pursuit of perfectionism!

Lifestyle Management

Living a healthy lifestyle is about making easy-to-manage healthy choices in your day-to-day living.

How we fuel our bodies is fundamental to promoting energy levels and maintaining overall good health.

Physical activity helps prevent some risk factors for heart disease: blood cholesterol, diabetes and hypertension. It can improve muscle and bone health, improve sleep and reduce stress.

Resting and good quality sleep will help you to recharge your batteries and feel better able to cope with everyday pressures.

Nourish yourself

Foods can help manage stress in several ways. Comfort and healthy foods, like a bowl of warm porridge, fruit and vegetables and dark chocolate can boost levels of serotonin. Other processed, caffeinated or sugary foods can exacerbate stress levels. A healthy diet can help counter the impact of stress by boosting the immune system and lowering blood pressure.

If you are looking for a simple way to unwind from your stress-filled life, try this: drink a glass of water.

The link between water and stress reduction is well-documented. All of your organs, including your brain, needs water to function properly. If you are dehydrated and your body isn't running well that can lead to unhealthy stress levels.

Consume Less

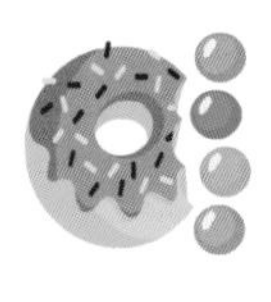

CARBONATED DRINKS

REFINED SUGARS

ARTIFICIAL FOODS

PROCESSED FOODS

Be active

A sedentary lifestyle isn't helpful when it comes to your personal well-being. Research has now identified that physical inactivity may increase the risks of certain cancers and contribute to anxiety and depression. People who engage in more physical activity are less likely to develop heart disease.

Exercise is vital for maintaining mental fitness, and it can reduce stress. Studies show that it is very effective at reducing fatigue, improving alertness and concentration, and enhancing overall cognitive function.

When stress affects the brain, with its many nerve connections, the rest of the body feels the impact as well. So it stands to reason that if your body feels better, so does your mind.

Being active doesn't necessarily mean a trip to the gym, just getting outside in the fresh air for a brisk walk can be very beneficial!

Devices to measure how many steps you walk a day can also be very motivating. Setting yourself a target to walk 10,000 steps a day is recommended for a healthy heart, as well as having positive effects on your mental health too.

Sleep well

Lack of good quality sleep can affect your memory, judgment and mood. Stress levels can increase when the length and quality of sleep decreases. Here are a few tips to help you sleep better:

- ✓ Take a warm bath (not too hot) and this will help your body reach a temperature that is ideal for rest.
- ✓ Write to-do lists for the next day so you can organise your thoughts and clear your mind of any distractions.
- ✓ If something is on your mind write a cons and pros list. Write down what is bothering you and any of the negatives and then flip it over and write down all the positives and potential opportunities.

- ✓ Do some relaxation exercises, such as light yoga stretches which can help to relax the muscles.
- ✓ Avoid exercising vigorously, as it will have the opposite effect.
- ✓ Listen to relaxation apps or podcasts with carefully narrated scripts and gentle hypnotic music and sound effects to relax you.
- ✓ Read a book or listen to music that relaxes the mind.
- ✓ Avoid mobile technology in the bedroom and get a separate alarm clock.
- ✓ Focus on breathing deeply and count your blessings one by one as you drift off to sleep.

Everyday Energy

It is also worth bearing in mind that personal energy is not just about physical energy. Consider a more holistic approach by looking at these four key areas and ask yourself the following questions:

Physical energy - how healthy are you?

Emotional energy - how happy are you?

Mental energy - how well can you focus on something?

Spiritual energy - are you true to your purpose and personal values?

It is important to know how much energy is in your personal tank and creating moments of sanctuary within your day will help you to replenish your resources and maintain balance.

Here are a few simple ways that can help you to recharge:

Practise mindfulness

The term mindfulness comes from Eastern spiritual and religious traditions. It is a very old concept and is a key part of Buddhism and also appears in Hindu writings.

A great deal of scientific research now shows that the mindful approach to stress, anxiety and mental health is a very helpful and popular way of dealing with and diffusing high levels of stress.

Mindfulness refers to being completely in touch with and aware of the present moment, as well as taking a non-evaluative and non-judgmental approach to your inner experience. It is essentially about being present and noticing what is around you. So often, if you are not careful, you can find yourself racing through life in a mad dash and not taking time to stop and really appreciate what is going on around you.

There are so many ways that you can live more mindfully. Here are four simple suggestions:

1. Begin each day with a beginners' mind
You can choose the day you want by clearing your mind, consciously letting go of any negativity and baggage and beginning each day with a fresh outlook and an open and uncluttered mind.

2. Choose to be present
Look up and around you, feel your feet on the ground, the air on your skin, the wonderment of your environment. Focus on the present moment and make a conscious effort to absorb yourself in it.

3. Breathe deeply
Take time to do some deep breathing. For a few minutes breathe in to the count of five and out to the count of five. This can help reduce stress and have a very calming effect.

4. Mindful engagement
Be present when you are with other people and really attend to listening to them with your undivided attention.

Unplug yourself

It is becoming increasingly obvious that our world is developing an unhealthy attachment to technology and mobile devices.

FOMO has been recognised as a recently emerging psychological disorder brought on by the advance of technology. It is an acronym standing for the expression fear of missing out. This is used to describe that feeling of anxiety which many people experience when they discover that other people are having fun together or are being successful at something. Unhealthy and unrealistic comparisons are then made.

FOMO can manifest itself in various ways, from a brief pang of envy through to resentment and a real sense of self-doubt or inadequacy.

Almost everything will work again if you unplug it for a while, including you!

Be grateful

With the advent of the positive psychology movement, gratitude has become a mainstream focus of research.

The main conclusions that have been drawn so far are that grateful people report higher levels of positive emotions, life satisfaction, vitality and optimism and lower levels of depression and stress. Cultivating an attitude of gratitude appears to enhance the feel-good factor.

Each day you are gifted 86,400 seconds. How many do you use to say thank you?

Taking time out each day to stop and focus on the things you are grateful for can help you to establish moments of calm and happiness.

There are many ways to practise gratitude. Keeping a daily journal, identifying and sharing the highlights of your day and simply making a point of being more appreciative can help you to absorb your daily dose of vitamin gratitude.

Rest

You have a limited amount of energy to expend, and if you are not careful you can end up pushing yourself beyond a healthy threshold. In order to keep generating more energy, you need to let your body rest.

Energy is like the fuel you put into your vehicle and if you don't keep refilling the tank, the car will eventually stop. Our bodies function in the same way.

We are designed to repair from the daily wear and tear we impose on ourselves, and this most often happens while we rest.

It is important to recognise the value of being a human being as opposed to a human doing!

Sometimes, if you want to go a bit faster, you need to slow down!

Take rest; a field that has
rested gives a bountiful crop
Ovid

If you feel 'burnout' setting in,
if you feel demoralised and
exhausted, it is best, for
the sake of everyone, to withdraw
and restore yourself. The point
is to have a long-term perspective

Dalai Lama